This Book Belongs To

_____

No Sad Secrets!

Justin learns what to do when keeping secrets make him sad

Written by : Sheryl Nadeen Henry

Illustrated by : Rajhean Rodriques

SDA
PUBLISHING

Published by: SDA Publishing

ISBN: 978-1-7363708-4-1

Dedication:

This book is dedicated to all the boys and girls who are still finding the courage to share the secrets that make them sad.

To my beloved nieces and nephew :

Akeem, Tiana, and Osheen

The very best is yet to come

My mommy says to me,
as I whisper in my brothers' ear
a juicy tale I have to share.

No Sad Secrets!
No Sad Secrets!
No Sad Secrets!

That's my daddy's rule.

It comes to my mind

when I joke with friends at school.

No Sad Secrets!
No Sad Secrets!
No Sad Secrets!

Never, ever, ever!
We only say things
that make us smile or make us clever.

My auntie says to me,
"Don't whisper stuff that's not quite so.
Tell the truth because God knows!"

No Sad Secrets!

No Sad Secrets!

No Sad Secrets!

My grandpa says to me,

"Always tell the things that make you hurt or want to cry, even if someone tells you to keep it all inside."

No Sad Secrets!

No Sad Secrets!

No Sad Secrets!

My grandma says to me,
"But don't you go around sharing grandma's recipes!"

No Sad Secrets!

No Sad Secrets!

No Sad Secrets!

Because they're just bad news!
Mommy says,
"Never keep a secret if you start to get the blues."

No Sad Secrets!
No Sad Secrets!
No Sad Secrets!

It's the family rule!
I always tell a grownup, when I'm angry,
scared, or sad. But I also like to share
when I'm excited and when I'm glad!

No Sad Secrets!
No Sad Secrets!
No Sad Secrets!

I won't tell a birthday wish
or what's on my Christmas list!
I won't say a word about mom's gift
or grandma's yummy special dish!

But if someone touched me in a scary way
and told me that I shouldn't say
I'd shout out with my loudest voice!

I'd tell my mom and I'd tell my dad,
My Cousin Lou and Auntie Fran
I would proclaim for all to hear!

That's the thing I will not do;
is keep a secret that hurts me or you;
Will you promise not to keep sad secrets too?

No Sad Secrets!
No Sad Secrets!
No Sad Secrets!

TAKE A CLOSER LOOK

What kinds of secrets do you like to keep?

_____

_____

_____

_____

Do you have any secrets that make you upset? Write them down so you can share with a grown-up you trust. (these are safe grown-ups).

_____

_____

_____

_____

Draw a picture of how you feel when you are :

ANGRY

SCARED

SAD

What are some things that you can do to help you feel better when you are angry, scared, or sad?

_____

_____

_____

_____

_____

Draw a picture of how you feel when you are happy, or excited.

NO SAD SECRETS PROMISE

I, _____

    (name)

promise to tell a grown up I trust if someone asks me to keep a secret that makes angry, scared, or sad.

Safe grown-ups I can share my sad secrets with :

1. _____

2. _____

3. _____

Parents and Care givers

Talk about the importance of the no sad-secret promise with your child, and help them identify safe adults they can trust to share their secrets.

No Sad Secrets!

Justin learns what to do when keeping secrets make him sad

This book teaches important skills to help children distinguish between secrets that are fun and safe to keep, and those that are important to share with a trusted adult.

Developing a plan, using exercises such as the ones provided in this book can help children feel more secure and in control of their safety. Additionally, the skills highlighted in this book also equips children with the information they need to respond appropriately in difficult situations; such as in instances of bullying or abuse.

If a child discloses abuse of any kind, get help immediately:

Call to report the abuse to your local authorities, and seek supportive counseling services for the child.

SDA
PUBLISHING